Reader Services

CUSTOMER SERVICE IN THE UK AND REPUBLIC OF IRELAND
How to continue your collection:
Customers can either place an order with their newsagent or receive issues on subscription.
Back issues: Either order through your newsagent or write to: Marvel Collection, Jacklin Enterprises UK, PO Box 77, Jarrow, NE32 3YH, enclosing payment of the cover price plus £1.00 p&p per copy. (Republic of Ireland: cover price plus €1.75). Subscriptions: You can have your issues sent directly to your home. For details, see insert in issue 1 or phone our Customer Service Hotline on 0871 472 4240 (Monday to Friday, 9am-5pm, calls cost 10p per minute from UK landline). Alternatively you can write to Marvel Collection, Jacklin Enterprises UK, PO Box 77, Jarrow, NE32 3YH, or fax your enquiries to 0871 472 4241, or e-mail: marvelcollection@jacklinservice.com or visit www.graphicnovelcollection.com

CUSTOMER SERVICE IN OVERSEAS MARKETS

Australia: Back issues can be ordered from your newsagent. Alternatively telephone (03) 9872 4000 or write to:
Back Issues Department, Bissett Magazine Services, PO Box 3460, Nunawading Vic 3131. Please enclose payment of the cover price, plus A$2.49 (inc. GST) per issue postage and handling. Back issues are subject to availability.
Subscriptions: You can have your issues sent directly to your home. For details, see insert in issue 1 or phone our Customer Service Hotline on (03) 9872 4000. Alternatively you can write to Hachette subs offer, Bissett Magazine Services, PO Box 3460, Nunawading Vic 3131, or fax your enquiries to (03) 9873 4988, or order online at www.bissettmags.com.au

New Zealand: For back issues, ask your local magazine retailer or write to: Netlink, PO Box 47906, Ponsonby, Auckland.
South Africa: Back issues are available through your local CNA store or other newsagent.
Subscriptions: call (011) 265 4309, fax (011) 314 2984, or write to: Marvel Collection, Private Bag 10, Centurion 0046 or e-mail: service@jacklin.co.za
Malta: Back issues are only available through your local newsagent.
Malaysia: Call (03) 8023 3260, or e-mail: sales@allscript.com
Singapore: Call (65) 287 7090, or e-mail: sales@allscript.com

Published by Hachette Partworks Ltd, Jordan House, 47 Brunswick Place, London, N1 6EB
www.hachettepartworks.co.uk

Distributed in the UK and Republic of Ireland by Marketforce

This special edition published in 2012 by Hachette Partworks Ltd. forming part of The Ultimate Marvel Graphic Novel Collection.

Printed in China.
ISBN: 978-1-906965-79-2

Licensed by Marvel Characters B.V. through Panini S.p.A., Italy. All Rights Reserved.

NEW X-MEN

GRANT MORRISON
WRITER

FRANK QUITELY & ETHAN VAN SCIVER
ARTIST

TIM TOWNSEND, MARK MORALES,
DAN GREEN & PRENTISS ROLLINS
INKS

HI-FI DESIGN
COLOURIST

COMICRAFT
LETTERS

MARK POWERS
EDITOR

JOE QUESADA
EDITOR IN CHIEF

New X-Men
E Is For Extinction

Marco M. Lupoi
*Panini Publishing Director
(Europe)*

Given the nature of the X-Men's origins, it is fitting that the title has constantly evolved over its lifetime. However when Grant Morrison took over the reins of *X-Men* in 2001, it wasn't so much evolution, but revolution!

Morrison has a reputation for introducing outlandish new concepts to super hero comics and discovering new angles to explore characters from. With *New X-Men*, he used his amazing skills of reinvention to successfully pull Marvel's X-franchise kicking and screaming into the new millennium. In Morrison's hands the X-Men became edgy again. It seemed anything could happen and often did – in an outrageous fashion! Tired clichés were put to rest by a slew of stories brimming with mind-blowing spectacle, storming angst and emotional drama.

For the first arc of *New X-Men*, the responsibility for bringing Morrison's high-concept mutant soap opera to life fell to artist Frank Quitely. Like Stan Lee and Jack Kirby or Alan Moore and Alan Davis, Morrison and Quitely are two creators who gel perfectly. No matter how complicated Morrison's scripts get, Quitely finds a way to clearly move the story along without losing any of the intricate details. A perfect example is Professor Xavier's psychic hijacking in the first issue. For a conflict that takes place purely within the confines of someone's mind, it still carries just as much intensity and excitement as any drawn-out, knockdown scrap between any two of Marvel's most physically powerful characters.

To this day, characters and concepts from Morrison's run are still having a dramatic effect on Marvel's mutants. It seems that *New X-Men* is a series that will most definitely survive the test of time and stand shoulder-to-shoulder with the likes of the *Dark Phoenix* saga as another defining moment in the X-Men's history.

ontains material originally published in magazine form as New X-Men #114-117. Senior Editor (Hachette Partworks Ltd.), Sarah Gale. Packaged by Panini Publishing, a division of Panini UK Limited. M
iddell, Managing Director. Alan O'Keefe, Managing Editor. Simon Frith, Senior Editor. Ed Hammond Editor. Marco M. Lupoi, Publishing Director Europe. Tim Warran-Smith, Designer. Additional content
ike Conroy & Jon Laury. Office of publication: Brockbourne House, 77 Mount Ephraim, Tunbridge Wells, Kent TN4 8BS. No similarity between any of the names, characters, persons and/or institutions
is edition with those of any living or dead person or institution is intended, and any such similarity which may exist is purely coincidental. This publication may not be sold, except by authorised dealers
nd is sold subject to the condition that it shall not be sold or distributed with any part of its cover or markings removed, nor in a mutilated condition.

THE STORY SO FAR...

Events leading up to New X-Men: E Is For Extinction

With each passing year more and more young teenagers are discovering that they are mutants, born with amazing powers that set them apart from normal humans.

One man, **Professor Charles Xavier** has made it his life's work to help these adolescents find their way in the world. As headmaster of the **Xavier Institute for Higher Learning,** he teaches young mutants to both control their new abilities and deal with a world that hates and fears them.

The school is also the base of operations for the **X-Men** – a team of mutant heroes who specialise in dealing with those who wish to use their powers for evil means and to protect other mutants from oppression.

One such method of oppression that the X-Men have faced in the past is the **Sentinels.** Created by **Bolivar Trask,** these robotic automatons were programmed to hunt down mutants. Over the years, they have been upgraded many times but the X-Men have always managed to defeat them.

In the last few months some mutants have undergone unexplained secondary mutations. The blue-furred, hyper intelligent **Beast** has changed appearance to a new feline form, telepath **Jean Grey** has now developed telekinetic powers and reformed-villain-turned-mutant-teacher **Emma Frost** is now able to change her skin into an unbreakable diamond form.

Recently, the mutant villain and long-time X-Men foe **Magneto** was granted sovereignty over the politically unstable island nation of **Genosha.** Declaring the island a mutant sanctuary, he successfully rallied an army and crushed the civil war that was tearing the country apart. Next, he intended to send his mutant army to war against humanity but was stopped by the X-Men. During the battle, Magneto was effectively crippled by a vicious attack from **Wolverine.** Now confined to a wheelchair, he oversees the island's development as it slowly transforms into the advanced civilisation he always hoped it would one day become.

Meanwhile, for the X-Men life returns to what passes for normal as they prepare for the beginning of a new school term...

NEW X-MEN #114
COVER ARTWORK

SCOTT SUMMERS/CYCLOPS

JEAN GREY

EMMA FROST

HENRY McCOY Phd/BEAST

LOGAN/WOLVERINE

E IS FOR EXTINCTION
ONE OF THREE

XAVIER
INSTITUTE
FOR
HIGHER LEARNING

BE CAREFUL WHERE YOU PUT YOUR *HEAD*, PROFESSOR.

THE CONTACTS ON THE *MINDPHONES* MAY FALL SHORT OF MY USUAL DEFT FINISH.

THESE BRUTISH PAWS AND I TAKE *FULL* RESPONSIBILITY IF YOUR EARLOBES ARE TORN TO FRINGES BY RAZOR-SHARP PLASTIC.

OTHERWISE... *CEREBRA* IS READY TO RUMBLE.

I *HAVE* NO EARLOBES, HENRY. PROCEED.

IF *CEREBRA* WORKS, SHE'LL *AMPLIFY* MY PSYCHIC SENSES TO THE *TENTH POWER*, IS THAT THE IDEA?

I VERY MUCH LOOK FORWARD TO EXPERIENCING THAT.

CEREBRA?

IMAGINE *CEREBRO'S* BIG SISTER; SHE CAN BOOST THE PROFESSOR'S MUTANT LOCATING ABILITIES TO *GLOBAL* RANGE.

...HUMOR ME, JEAN, I'M HORMONALLY-IMBALANCED.

YOU'RE INCREDIBLY *UPBEAT* FOR SOMEONE WHO'S TURNING INTO THE ROMANTIC LEAD FROM *"BEAUTY AND THE BEAST ON ICE,"* IF THAT'S WHAT YOU WANT ME TO SAY.

SODA?

DIET, PLEASE.

DIET? YOU WEIGH SIX HUNDRED POUNDS.

SO? DO I WANT TO GET *FAT?* I DO A LOT OF LEAPING AROUND.

I SUSPECT MY *LATEST* BEAST FORM IS CONNECTED TO THIS YEAR'S MUTANT *BABY BOOM.*

SUNSPOT ACTIVITY, MANIC DEPRESSIVE MOOD SWINGS; I FEEL LIKE A HINDU SEX GOD, JEAN.

I'M GOING TO WRITE A *PAPER* WHEN I RELEARN HOW TO USE A PEN.

THE NEW LOOK *SUITS* YOU, HANK.

DISTINGUISHED. FELINE. I LIKE IT.

IT ALL SEEMS PRETTY NATURAL.

EVERYTHING OKAY, PROFESSOR...? YOU KNOW WHAT *JEAN* AND I ARE LIKE ONCE WE GET STARTED.

I'M FINE. JOIN ME IN MY MIND AND TAKE A *LOOK* FOR YOURSELF, HENRY.

YOUR *CEREBRA* NETWORK'S LIKE A *GLOBAL POSITIONING SYSTEM*, THE RADIANT PEAKS ARE *MUTANT* WAVEFORMS.

WE'RE OBSERVING THE DISTINCTIVE SIGNATURE OF THE *X-GENE* WHICH GIVES EACH OF US OUR SPECIAL *GIFTS*, AM I CORRECT?

THIS IS *VERY* UNUSUAL, CHARLES.

YOUR THOUGHTS ARE ACTUALLY FORMING SOME KIND OF *CONDENSATION* ON THE WALLS ALL AROUND YOU.

I *MISSED* IT. THERE'S *SOMETHING...* AROUND COLOMBIA... *ECUADOR*, PERHAPS... I *THOUGHT* I FELT A TRACE, BUT...

ENHANCE *X200*.

IT MUST HAVE BEEN A TRICK OF THE TWINKLE IN YOUR EYES, HANK.

IT WAS LIKE A *FLARE*...A GENETIC *FLARE*...SOMEONE COULD BE IN TROUBLE.

I REALLY *DID* S SOMETHING...

THE VIEW'S INCREDIBLE.

ALL THOSE LIGHTS ARE NEWLY EMERGING MUTANTS, JEAN...

WHAT'S *THAT*?

WHAT'S THAT *BIG* ONE? USE THE *ZOOM.* I JUST SAW THIS *ENORMOUS* SPIKE IN SOUTH AMERICA.

PROFESSOR?

LOOK AT THE WORLD. THERE ARE SO *MANY* MUTANTS OUT THERE, HANK.

MORE AND MORE OF US ALL THE TIME.

I WONDER WHAT IT MEANS?

SCOTT AND LOGAN ARE ON THEIR WAY HOME FROM RESCUE OPERATIONS IN *AUSTRALIA.*

WHY DON'T WE ASK THEM TO LOOK IN ON YOUR FLARE, HENRY?

I'VE **NEVER** BEEN LUCKY DOWN UNDER.

BUT HEY...ENOUGH ABOUT **MY** LOVE LIFE. TELL YOUR GRANDKIDS YOU JUST WALKED AWAY FROM A **SENTINEL** ATTACK, BUB. THAT'S IF IT DIDN'T SCARE YOU **STERILE.**

...THING WAS AS TALL AS A HOUSE.

YOU'RE **X-MEN?**

HE'S **WOLVERINE.** I'M **CYCLOPS.**

STEVE. MY MATES MOSTLY CALL ME **UGLY JOHN.**

X-MEN.

NO **SMOKING** PLEASE, WOLVERINE.

YOU HAVE RAPID-HEALING GIFTS, THE REST OF US AR RUNNING ON **LUNGS.**

I CAN'T **HELP** SMOKING, SPACE CAD SUMMERS.

THE BIG, BAD **SENTINEL** SET ME ON **FIRE,** REMEMBER?

I'M DEALING WITH THE EMOTIONAL AND PHYSICAL SIDE EFFECTS IN MY OWN WAY.

>NNN< SENTINEL HARDWARE'S GETTING **OLD...** FIVE THOUSAND ROUNDS OF LIVE AMMUNITION, TWO DEATH RAYS, FOUR INDEPENDENT **ROLLS ROYCE** ENGINES, THREE MILLION DOLLARS WORTH OF **RAM...**

>NNF< FIVE MINUTES LATER, IT'S **RUST** ON MY KNUCKLES.

LET'S HOPE THOSE WERE SOME OF THE LAST SENTINELS WE'LL EVER SEE. THEY LOOKED LIKE DECOMMISSIONED GOVERNMENT ORDNANCE.

ROGUE MACHINES LEFT OVER FROM THE BIG MUTANT **WITCHHUNTS** A FEW MONTHS BACK.

GET OUT OF MY HEAD OR I'LL *FIRE*.

YOU *WOULD* TOO, WOULDN'T YOU?

WELL... THIS IS ONLY HOW IT *STARTS*.

ARE YOU VERY AFRAID NOW?

AAUUUU

CHARLES!

>GUHH<

OH MY GOD... OUR THOUGHTS ARE BLEEDING...TORN... CHARLES...?

WHAT WAS THAT... MINDQUAKE... I JUST FELT?

WHERE DID THAT GUN COME FROM?

PLEASE DON'T COME ANY FURTHER INTO THESE... THOUGHTS, JEAN...

ARE THESE WORDS FROM THE FUTURE? PLEASE, JEAN.

PURE APPALLING HATRED, *UNSTOPPABLE*...

...SCOTT... LOGAN...

IT'S THERE... HENRY WAS RIGHT... WARN THEM, JEAN... WARN *EVERYONE*... IT'S IN ECUADOR...

I'M BEING EATEN *ALIVE* BY ENORMOUS INSECTS AND... AND THERE ARE *SOUNDS* OUT THERE...

YOU LED ME TO BELIEVE I'D BE PERFORMING *BLACK OPS* ROOT CANAL WORK ON THE *PRESIDENT.*

WHAT ARE WE DOING IN A GUERRILLA WAR ZONE?

STOP QUIVERING, MR. TRASK. *NO* REBEL FORCES REMAIN. *NO* LOYALIST TROOPS ARE LEFT ALIVE.

THERE'S ONLY A *SCRAPYARD* HERE, SCAVENGED AND STRIPPED OF RAW MATERIALS BY THE *MASTER MOLD.*

YOU KEEP SAYING THAT.

WHAT DOES EVOLUTION HAVE TO DO WITH DENTISTRY? WHERE ARE WE *GOING*

YOU'RE HERE FOR A REASON, DON'T WORRY.

IMAGINE SELF-MADE SENTINELS, USING SPARE PARTS TO *EVOLVE* THEMSELVES INTO MORE *EFFECTIVE* FORMS.

I DON'T THINK I WANT TO...

WHAT'S THAT NOISE?

LOOK, I DEMAND TO BE TAKEN BACK TO SAFETY...

IT'S LIKE A *MONSTER* WASP... IT'S...

...LIKE SOME HORRIBLE GIANT LAWNMOWER...

URRRRR

IT'S THEM. WILD SENTINELS. *LOOK* AT THEM.

I CAN'T... I CAN'T... ÷UNNH÷

OH GOD... YOU'RE CRAZY ÷UNNH÷

DON'T WASTE ANY TEARS ON THE SOLDIER-BOYS; THEY CAME *PRE*-DECEASED. THEY MAKE ME LOOK *OFFICIAL*, SO I MARCH THE CORPSES AROUND WITH MY *THOUGHTS*.

SEE HOW THE FAMILY ANDROIDS HAVE GROWN UP, MR. TRASK?

GO ON, MEET HUMANKIND'S LAST HOPE AGAINST THE MUTANT MENACE.

TALK TO THEM, MR. TRASK! OR THEY'LL CHOP YOU UP AND GRIND YOU INTO NEATLY FILED SEGMENTS.

NOOO DON'T HURT ME IN THE NAME OF GOD STOP THEM STOP

AMM

AH

ANH

VOCAL IDENTIFICATION: TRASK.

PRIME COMMAND PROTOCOLS SEARCH: ONLINE.

RUNNING PROTOCOLS: STOP.

PRESERVE TRASK D.N.A.

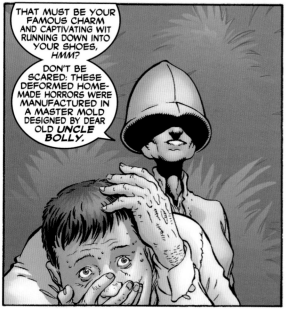

THAT MUST BE YOUR FAMOUS CHARM AND CAPTIVATING WIT RUNNING DOWN INTO YOUR SHOES, HMM?

DON'T BE SCARED: THESE DEFORMED HOME-MADE HORRORS WERE MANUFACTURED IN A MASTER MOLD DESIGNED BY DEAR OLD UNCLE BOLLY.

PRESERVE TRASK D.N.A.

THEY'LL DO ANYTHING YOU SAY, MR. TRASK. I BROUGHT YOU HERE IN MY CAPACITY AS A BIOLOGIST BECAUSE I FEEL IT'S YOUR DUTY TO SAVE THE HUMAN SPECIES.

THEY'RE NOT ATTACKING YOU.

WHY BE THE SMALL MAN WHEN YOU COULD BE THE SCOURGE AND DESTROYER OF MONSTERS?

THESE ANDROID ASSASSINS HAVE OBVIOUSLY REACHED THE LIMITS OF THEIR ABILITY TO EVOLVE IN THIS ENVIRONMENT.

WITH A WORD, YOU CAN EXTEND THEIR REACH.

WITH A WORD, YOU CAN EXTERMINATE HOMO SUPERIOR IN ITS INFANCY...WHILE THE SPECIES IS STILL TOO YOUNG TO FIGHT BACK.

SO LOWER THAT ONCE-COMMANDING VOICE OF YOURS A FEW OCTAVES.

NEW X-MEN #115
COVER ARTWORK

LOGAN
WOLVERINE

HANK McCOY
BEAST

EMMA FROST
WHITE QUEEN

E IS FOR EXTINCTION
TWO OF THREE

WHAT HAPPENED?

ONE MINUTE I'M FOLLOWING THROUGH INTO MY CALVINS UNDER A GIANT ROBOT SENTINEL HAND IN SYDNEY HARBOR, THEN I'M IN SPACE.

AND HERE COME SOME OF THEM NOW.

CHARLES XAVIER
PROFESSOR X

JEAN GREY
PHOENIX

SCOTT SUMMERS
CYCLOPS

GO BACK TO SLEEP, *UGLY JOHN,* WE LIKE YOU BETTER THAT--

DID SOMETHING JUST *HIT* US?

IT'S A *SENTINEL.*

YOU KNOW WHAT I ADMIRE **MOST** ABOUT YOU, SUMMERS?

⇥SUHH⇤

YOUR ICY CALM LUNACY UNDER PRESSURE.

CALL ME **CYCLOPS** DURING MISSIO **WOLVERINE.** KEEPS THIN(STRAIGHT.

CALL THIS A **MISSION?**

⇥NUHH!⇤

ALL I KNOW IS, WE CAN'T LET THEM TURN X-WING 8 TECHNOLOGY INTO **SPARE PARTS.**

SCOTT SUMMERS: CYCLOPS: VOICE KEY FOR AUTO DESTRUCT.

LOGAN?

LOGAN: WOLVERINE: VOICE KEY FOR AUTO-DESTRUCT.

VOICE KEYS ACCEPTED.

I DON'T **BELIEVE** THIS.

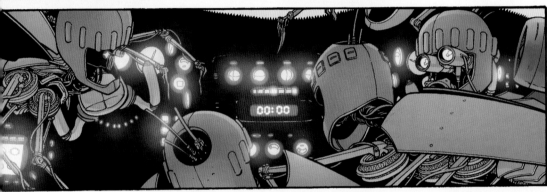

OKAY.

HOW DO WE GET HIM OUT OF *THIS?*

NOTHING MUCH HERE: OLD CANS... SCRAP AND SALVAGE AND SOME ELECTRONICS.

YOU EVER SEE A SENTINEL LOOK ANYTHING LIKE THIS?

I'VE SEEN ENOUGH. SENTINELS *HUNT* MUTANTS, LOGAN.

THEY *KNOW* WE'RE HERE. I FIGURE OUR ONLY OPTION IS TO DISABLE THE MASTER MOLD.

SO WHOSE IDEA WAS IT TO DIVERT VIA ECUADOR WITH A CIVILIAN IN TOW?

≥URRR≤

OH --

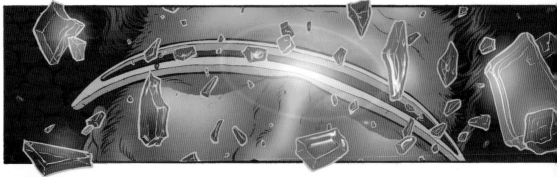

WELL HANDLED.

STAY RIGHT WHERE YOU ARE, UGLY JOHN.

I'LL TRY *TALKIN'* 'EM DOWN.

≥UHNNHN≤

MUTANT SPECIMEN LOCATED AND CONTAINED.

≥URRR≤

"DEAR TRISH--"

"--SO GOOD TO HEAR YOUR VOICE AGAIN..." NO, SCRATCH THAT...

"DEAR TRISH, JUST GOT DONE WATCHING YOUR INCREDIBLE ACCOUNT OF THE WAR IN GENOSHA.

"CONGRATULATIONS ON THE AWARD NOMINATION. THIS KIND OF RECOGNITION HAS BEEN LONG OVERDUE FOR YOU.

"I'VE BEEN THROUGH A LOT OF CHANGES, TOO, SINCE WE LAST HOOKED UP. SOMETIMES I FEEL LIKE I'M SOARING THROUGH THE STRATOSPHERE--

"--ON THE BRIGHTEST, SUNNIEST DAY OF MY LIFE. THE NEXT MOMENT I'M DIVING IN A BLUE SUBMARINE TO THE DARKEST DEPTHS OF MY SOUL."

A "BLUE SUBMARINE"? NO, HANK, NO...

HANG ON. STOP. SAVE.

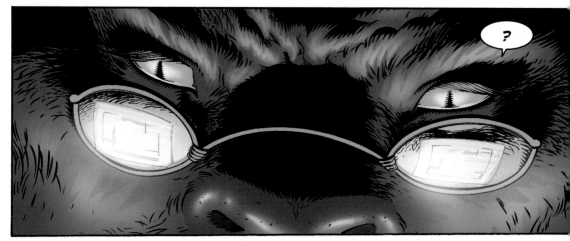

?

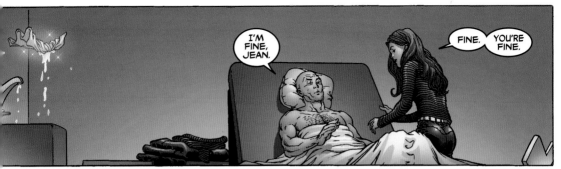

I'M FINE, JEAN.

FINE. YOU'RE FINE.

ONE MINUTE YOUR BRAIN IS BLEEDING THROUGH BOTH NOSTRILS, THE NEXT YOU'RE FINE.

AND WHY DIDN'T YOU *TELL* US YOU CARRIED A GUN?

IT'S NOT WHAT YOU THINK, JEAN. I WOULD *NEVER* USE IT ON ANOTHER LIVING CREATURE, YOU KNOW THAT.

...T MY BRAIN, YOU ...DERSTAND... MY ...AIN IS A LETHAL ...EAPON. IF SOME ...ENEMY WERE TO *HIJACK* IT...

I HAVE TO BE PREPARED TO MAKE THE ULTIMATE SACRIFICE, IF NEED BE.

OR THE ULTIMATE *GAMBLE.*

IT'S ESSENTIAL I GET BACK TO CEREBRA, JEAN. I MUST IDENTIFY THIS NEW MUTANT MIND I ENCOUNTERED BEFORE IT CAUSES ANY MORE DAMAGE.

FETCH MY CHAIR!

THAT TONE OF VOICE MIGHT WORK WITH SCOTT, BUT NOT WITH ME.

YOU'RE IN NO FIT *CONDITION* TO...

SORRY TO INTERRUPT...

WE JUST LOST RADIO CONTACT WITH SCOTT AND LOGAN, AND THE X-WING IS OFF RADAR...

THEN CEREBRA IS OUR ONLY MEANS OF CONTACTING OUR PEOPLE.

MY CHAIR, PLEASE, HENRY!

IS IT *EVIL*, MS. NOVA? WHAT I'VE JUST DONE... SOME PEOPLE WOULD CALL IT EVIL, WOULDN'T THEY?

WERE THE DOCTORS WHO WIPED OUT THE ENTIRE SMALLPOX SPECIES EVIL?

IN A WORLD WITHOUT VALUES OR MORALITY, GOOD AND EVIL ARE JUST CHOICES ON THE MENU OF THE MIGHTY, MR. TRASK.

WHEN THEY HEAR *WHY* YOU LAUNCHED FOUR SUPERSONIC DEATH MACHINES INTO THE MOST DENSELY POPULATED MUTANT AREA ON EARTH...

...I THINK THEY'LL SAY "BY GOD, HE WAS EVIL, YES... BUT EVIL IN A *GOOD* WAY."

I WOKE UP A DENTIST... AND SOON I'LL BE THE WORLD'S GREATEST MASS MURDERER.

THEY SAY PEOPLE CAN COMMIT *ANY* ATROCITY GIVEN THE RIGHT EXCUSE...

IT'S A SPECIAL FEELING, ISN'T IT?

BEHIND THE MASK OF LIBERAL RESPECTABILITY, WITH ITS SAFE OPINIONS, WE *ALL* HATE THE MUTATIONS, DON'T WE?

HOW CAN IT BE *MURDER* WHEN THEY'RE GERMS OR VERMIN?

THERE WON'T BE TIME FOR THEM TO FEEL PAIN, WILL THERE?

IT WILL BE HUMANE?

IT DOESN'T SEEM REAL...

I KNOW HOW MUCH ALL THIS... SUDDEN POWER *EXCITES* YOU, MR. TRASK.

I'D KNOW IT EVEN IF I COULDN'T READ YOUR MIND LIKE A T-SHIRT.

I EVEN KNOW YOU DREAM OF KEEPING MUTANT WOMEN AND CHILDREN AS *SLAVES* IN YOUR BASEMENT.

~TUCCHH~

I DON'T HATE YOU, DONALD TRASK THE THIRD. DOES THE GOURMET HATE THE STEAK?

BUT IT'S TAKEN ME TEN HOURS TO READ AND COPY THE THREE BILLION BASE LETTERS IN YOUR *DNA* SEQUENCE.

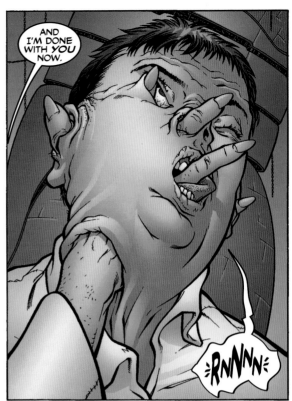

AND I'M DONE WITH *YOU* NOW.

~RNNNN~

DO YOU WANT TO KNOW THE *REAL* MESSAGE OF EVOLUTION?

~HUuull~

ALL LIFE WINDS UP AS MANURE.

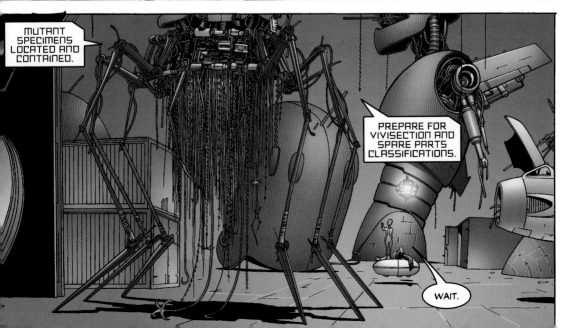

MUTANT SPECIMENS LOCATED AND CONTAINED.

PREPARE FOR VIVISECTION AND SPARE PARTS CLASSIFICATIONS.

WAIT.

VOCAL IDENTIFICATION: TRASK.

PRIME COMMAND PROTOCOLS SEARCH: ONLINE.

RUNNING PROTOCOLS: STOP.

PRESERVE TRASK DNA.

WELL...

...IN RUINS... SOURCES IN CAPE TOWN, SOUTH AFRICA, SAY PARTS OF THE CITY WERE DEVASTATED BY THE ATTACK...

THE ORIGINAL SENTINELS WERE RESTRICTED BY THEIR SIZE AND SHAPE.

THESE WILD SENTINELS CAN ADAPT AND ASSUME ANY FORM NECESSARY TO ENGAGE AND DESTROY THE MUTANT MENACE.

≋URRRR≋

MENACES LIKE *YOU*.

AM I REALLY TO BELIEVE YOU'RE FROM CHARLES XAVIER'S SCHOOL FOR THE GIFTED?

WHAT *ARE* YOU? THE X-MASCOT?

EYEWITNESS ACCOUNTS... GARBLED... FANTASTIC...

MONSTROUS THINGS OF GLASS AND STEEL AND FIRE... ON THEIR WAY SOUTH...

OH NO.

NO NO. I SHOULDN'T BE HERE. I'M FROM AUSTRALIA.

DON'T *HURT* ME, MISSUS. DON'T HURT ME...

THEY THINK *I'M* A TRASK TOO, YOU SEE.

THE MOST POWERFUL MUTANT-HUNTING MACHINES ON THIS ENTIRE PLANET WILL NOW DO ANYTHING *I* TELL THEM TO.

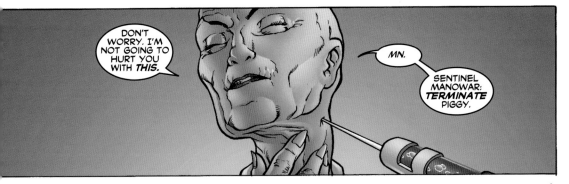

DON'T WORRY. I'M NOT GOING TO HURT YOU WITH *THIS.*

MN.

SENTINEL MANOWAR: *TERMINATE* PIGGY.

NNNNEEEUUU

WELL, *THAT* WORKS.

NEXT.

UNN...

‡SNFF‡

BACON?

SENTINEL *MANOWAUUURCHCH‡*

ALL I GOTTA DO IS THINK AND *ADAMANTIUM RAZORS* BURST THROUGH THE SKIN OF MY KNUCKLES AT ONE HUNDRED AND THIRTY MILES PER HOUR, BABE.

SO YOU BETTER *RELAX.*

SUMMERS!

FOR THE LOVE OF GOD, THE KID'S DYING IN *AGONY.*

AUUUUUUUUUUU

IT'S OKAY, LOGAN.

FUUUHAUUUU

JOHN... STEVE... I'M SO SORRY.

I KNOW THERE'S SOMETHING *MORE* THAN JUST THIS WORLD.

DEEP BREATH, DON'T BE SCARED.

JUST LOOK INTO MY EYES.

AS X-MEN, WE'RE TRAINED TO **HELP** MUTANTS IN TROUBLE. WE'VE ALSO BEEN TRAINED TO PREVENT GENETIC THREATS LIKE YOU FROM HURTING PEOPLE.

I'VE REMOVED MY EMERGENCY RUBY QUARTZ CONTACTS, WHICH LEAVES ME **BLIND.**

BUT I KNOW EXACTLY WHERE YOU ARE, AND SO HELP ME, I'LL GUT YOU WITH A BLINK OF MY EYES IF YOU TRY TO HURT ANYONE **ELSE.**

IT'S TOO **LATE.**

LOOK AROUND: THIS PLACE WAS MAKING 'EM BIGGER AND BETTER AN' THE ONLY THING SENTINELS LIKE TO DO BIGGER AND BETTER IS KILL MUTANTS!

YOU **SAW** WHAT SHE DID TO PIG-BOY! STONE COLD, SUMMERS!

LOOK AT HER! WHAT'S SO FUNNY?

WHAT **ELSE** DID THIS PSYCHO DO THAT SHE THINKS IS SO FUNNY?

WHERE DID SHE SEND THOSE SENTINELS?

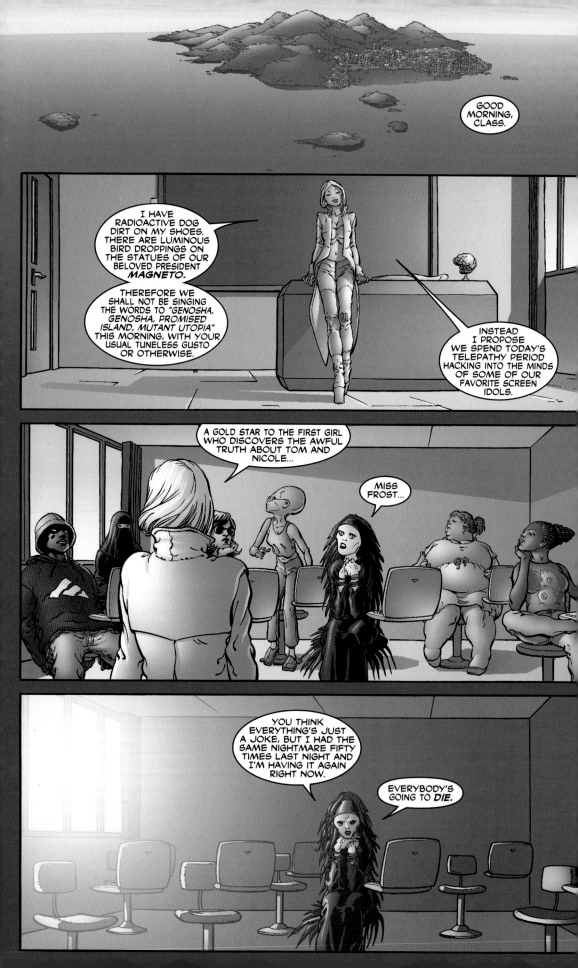

EXTERMINATION EVENT UNDERWAY.

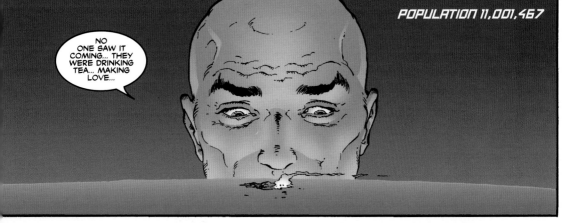

TARGET GENOSHA: POPULATION 16,521,063: FALLING.

POPULATION 11,001,467

NO ONE SAW IT COMING... THEY WERE DRINKING TEA... MAKING LOVE...

8,290,025

800,000

763...

ALL THOSE LIGHTS... GOING OUT... NO ONE SAW...

NEW X-MEN #116
COVER ARTWORK

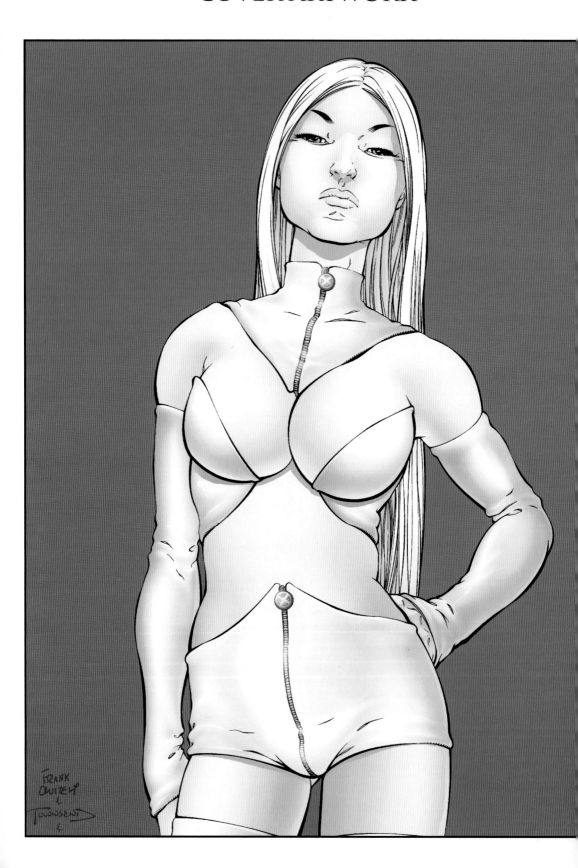

STAN LEE PRESENTS:

NEW

E IS FOR EXTINCTION OF

GRANT MORRISON
WRITER

FRANK QUITELY
PENCILER

MARK MORALES DAN GREEN
INKS

MEN

RADIATION LEVELS ARE OFF THE SCALE... THE MAP SAYS THIS WAS "MAGDA SQUARE," WHICH MEANS THOSE VITRIFIED SPIRES OVER THERE MUST BE *MAGNETO'S PALACE.*

YOU CAN SEE THIS THROUGH MY EYES, *PROFESSOR.*

GENOSHA IS *GONE.*

THEY FOUND OUT WHO *DID* THIS.

SCOTT AND LOGAN BROUGHT SOME WOMAN IN...

WAIT...

SO YOU SAY, BUT THAT'S ONE OF THE FIRST KNOWN SIGNS OF *PARANOID SCHIZOPHRENIA* INDUCED BY THE SIGHT OF MUTANT FAT DRIPPING FROM THE TWISTED BUS SHELTERS, JEAN.

I CAN SEE SOMEONE... SHINING.

HER NAME IS ELLIE PHIMISTER. HER MUTANT NAME IS NEGASONIC TEENAGE WARHEAD. SHE CHOSE IT *HERSELF*...

SHE WILL BE A CREDIT TO HER FAMILY AND OTHER SPECIES.

GET HER TO A *HOSPITAL.*

HER *SKIN...* WHAT'S THAT ALL OVER HER SKIN...

SHE'S A *ROBOT.* SHE MIGHT BE A SENTINEL.

GET HER TO A HOSPITAL...

THE KID'S DEAD...

THEN BRING HER BACK TO *LIFE,* YOU IMBECILE!

MY GOD. *EMMA FROST!*

EMMA! SHE'S *ONE* OF US, X-MEN!

SHE'S BEEN DEAD FOR HOURS.

EMMA?

IT'S ME... JEAN. *JEAN GREY.*

EMMA, WHAT ARE YOU *DOING* HERE? WHAT HAPPENED TO YOUR SKIN?

I HAVE NO *IDEA.*

IT GOT HARD.

WHAT *HAPPENED* TO EVERYTHING?

YOU SEVERED HER VOCAL CORDS, *WOLVERINE?*

EXECUTIVE DECISION, CHUCK. SHE WAS VOICE-ACTIVATING THE SENTINELS.

SHE'S GOT HER OWN PERSONAL HEALING GIFTS. AND RIGHT NOW THEY'RE WORKING HARD TO FIX UP THE TISSUE DAMAGE, SO WE DON'T HAVE MUCH TIME TO STAND AROUND FLAPPING OUR GUMS.

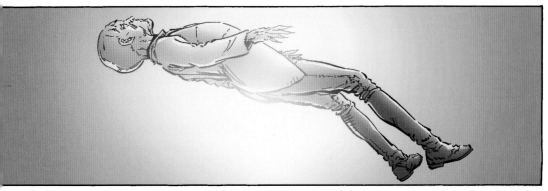

SIXTEEN MILLION MUTANTS ARE DEAD.

WHY?

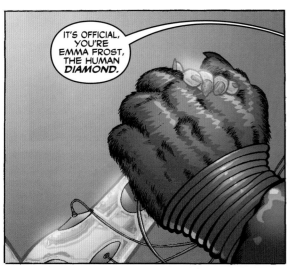

IT'S OFFICIAL, YOU'RE EMMA FROST, THE HUMAN *DIAMOND.*

EXCUSE ME; ORGANIC *WHAT?*

"SECONDARY MUTATION" WHAT? WHY HAVE THESE TOPICS NEVER BEFORE ENTERED ANY CONVERSATION IN CONNECTION WITH MY LIFE, HENRY?

YOUR PSEUDO-MEDICAL EXPLANATIONS ARE *FAR* FROM SATISFACTORY, MR. McCOY.

AND AS FOR YOUR BREATH...

DR. McCOY, EMMA. PATIENCE, PLEASE.

I KNOW YOU'VE BEEN THROUGH A LOT.

WE SAW GENOSHA. WE'RE STILL COUNTING THE DEAD AND TRYING TO FIGURE OUT WHO WE'VE *LOST.*

SO...I'M LOOKING INTO THIS, AND I'M TRYING TO DO A MILLION THINGS ALL AT ONCE.

JEAN CAN MOVE THINGS AROUND WITH HER MIND AGAIN, YOU'VE GROWN AN EXOSKELETON OF INVULNERABLE ORGANIC JEWELRY.

I, FOR MY SINS, HAVE MAGICALLY TRANSFORMED INTO TONY THE TIGER ON BARBITURATES!

FORGIVE ME, HENRY. GRIEF SO OFTEN MAKES ONE SHRILL AND *JUDGMENTAL.*

I DO LOOK RATHER *SPECTACULAR* IN THE LIGHT, DON'T I?

...UT...I SAW *CHILDREN* ...UT INTO WAFER-THIN ...LICES. I WATCHED A ...IFTED TEN-YEAR-OLD ...PIANIST SEARCH FOR HIS *HANDS* AMONG THE BROKEN GLASS.

THAT MONSTER MUST *DIE.*

KILLING OUR ENEMIES WAS MAGNETO'S WAY.

HE'S DEAD, EMMA. YOU WERE THERE. HIS *PHILOSOPHIES* DIED *WITH* HIM.

OH, COME *ON*, JEAN! *HUMANS* MADE THOSE SENTINELS TO KILL MUTANTS. THAT... THING IN YOUR CELLS GAVE THE *ORDER.*

I KNOW. AND GENOSHA IS GONE: SO THE ONLY WAY *LEFT* NOW IS THE PROFESSOR'S WAY.

WE NEED YOUR STRENGTH AND BRILLIANCE TO HELP US *RECOVER* FROM THIS.

≑TT≑ WE *ALL* KNEW SOMETHING LIKE THIS WOULD HAPPEN IN THE END! THEY'RE WIPING US *OUT!*

ENOUGH.

I'VE CALLED A TAXI TELEPATHICALLY, JEAN.

I'VE BECOME THE PERFECT FABERGE KILLING MACHINE FOR A REASON...

...AND THAT REASON IS SURELY NOT TO WAVE THE FLAG FOR X-LIBERALISM.

WHAT MAKES YOU SUCH A BITCH, EMMA?

BREEDING, DARLING.

TOP CLASS BREEDING

OKAY... SHE'S FROM BEYOND THE BIOLOGICAL TWILIGHT ZONE.

SHE *LOOKS* HUMAN ON THE OUTSIDE, BUT NOTHING LIKE HER HAS EVER EXISTED BEFORE.

AND SHE PREYS ON MUTANTS.

WHY

BECAUSE EVERY FEW HUNDRED THOUSAND YEARS, *EVOLUTION,* WHICH EMPATHETICALLY DOES *NOT* PROCEED SMOOTHLY, TAKES HUGE CATASTROPHIC *JUMPS.*

OLD LIFE FORMS GET WIPED FROM THE FOSSIL RECORD OVERNIGHT IN PERIODIC MASS EXTINCTIONS, AND ARE *REPLACED.*

I THINK *CASSANDRA NOVA* IS THE *FIRST* OF A NEW UNFORESEEN SPECIES.

I THINK SHE'LL *INSTINCTIVELY* USE HER OUTLANDISH NATURAL GIFTS TO WIPE US OUT IF SHE CAN.

THIS COULD BECOME A WAR FOR TH' DOMINATION OF THE BIOSPHE

DOMINATION? WAR? HENRY...

CAN'T WE THINK OF A *BETTER* WAY TO DEAL WITH THIS?

JEAN HAS A POINT...

THEY'RE TRYING TO RUIN THE DRAMATIC ATMOSPHERE, HANK IGNORE 'EM.

DOES SHE HUNT *PEOPLE?*

IF SHE HAS TO, MAYBE, BUT SHE DOESN'T REALLY *NEED* TO. AND THAT'S THE *SCARY* PART OF THE STORY...

...HUMANS ARE NO THREAT TO HER BECAUSE SHE INSTINCTIVELY *KNOWS* WHAT I JUST DISCOVERED.

MEANING *WHAT?*

MEANING **THIS**...I THINK I'VE FOUND A GENETIC TRIGGER FOR EXTINCTION BURIED DEEP IN THE HUMAN GENOME.

THIS E-GENE TURNS ON WHEN AN ENTIRE SPECIES IS ABOUT TO BE TURNED **OFF** BY MOTHER NATURE. THE DATA LOOKS CONCLUSIVE.

THE HUMAN RACE IS AT AN **END**.

WITHIN THREE, MAYBE FOUR GENERATIONS, THEY'LL BE GONE, REPLACED BY **US**. OR SOMETHING EVEN **STRANGER**.

SOMETHING LIKE CASSANDRA NOVA.

HUMAN BEINGS ARE DYING OUT?

TELL ME ONE MORE THING BEFORE I TAKE HER HEAD OFF. HOW COME SHE LOOKS LIKE **YOU**, CHUCK?

WELL, SEE, I THINK I CAN... CAN FEEL... TOO... FUNNY...BAD SMELL IN MY EYES...

INSIDE-OUT THOUGHTS... JEAN... HELP... HEAD...

HANK?

HANK.

CHECK.

LOGAN.

oOOWW!

HELL-WELLO...

UFF!

...WELCOME TO THE BLACK BUG ROOM.

EVERYONE HAS THEIR OWN BLACK BUG ROOM.

THIS IS YOURS, SCOTT.

JEAN... NO...

AAUUU!

JEAN, LISTEN TO ME.

THERE ARE THINGS WE NEED TO TALK ABOUT.

ABOUT OUR RELATIONSHIP... JEAN, LISTEN... THE BUGS SAY...

∋SPPFFLL∈

SNAP *OUT* OF IT, SCOTTIE.

TAKE CHARGE! THE BAD GUY IS *KILLING* WOLVERINE!

JEAN, COME BACK TO US. THINK.

THINK ABOUT THE OXYGEN MOLECULES... GETTING *FASTER* AROUND CASSANDRA. MAKE THEM GO FASTER, BABY.

...FASSR AND FASSER...

TEAAAM!

LOGAN, STAY STILL.

I HAVE ENOUGH PAINKILLERS HERE TO SEND A BRONTOSAURUS TO HAPPYLAND.

≈URRNNN≈

SAVE 'EM FOR YOUR BRONTOSAURUS, BUB... SHE'S GETTING AWAY...

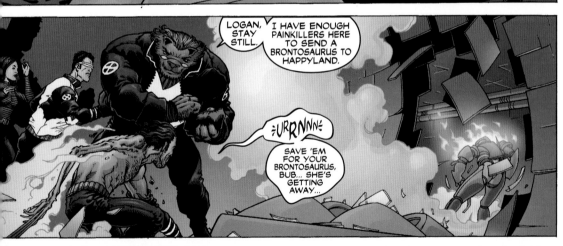

I KNOW YOU'RE JUST SOME *@$&%#-UP THING THAT WANTS TO SURVIVE...

WRONG PLACE. WRONG TIME.

SEE WHAT SHE'S TRYING TO DO! IF SHE REACHES THE CEREBRA SYSTEM, HER POWER WILL BE AMPLIFIED...

OH, DEAR LORD, NO... SCOTT...

CHARLES... DON'T GO...YOU MUSTN'T...

IT'S OKAY. SHH.

RRRNN?

CEREBRA!

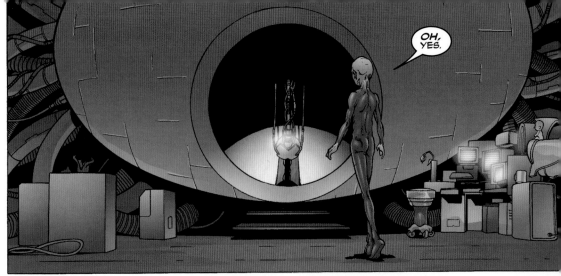

OH, YES.

DEAR CHARLES...

FROM HERE I CAN REACH OUT, TAKE HOLD OF EVERY REMAINING MUTANT MIND ON EARTH AND *EXTINGUISH* IT.

BUT I ONLY WANT *ONE*.

HAUUCH!

THERE ARE SOME THINGS YOU JUST SHOULDN'T BE ALLOWED TO GET *AWAY* WITH.

YOU OKAY WITH THIS?

SHE HAD TO BE NEUTRALIZED, LOGAN. EMMA... I *KNEW* YOU WOULDN'T TURN YOUR BACK ON US.

SWEET AS YOU ARE, I DIDN'T COME BACK FOR *YOU*, SCOTT. I CAME FOR MY HANDBAG.

LUCKY FOR YOU, THIS IS A LOUIS VUITTON...

HEY. SHE HAS *HEALING* GIFTS RIGHT...?

AUUM... UMMA... UMMMMM CHARLES...

...NUUUUU...

IT KILLED SIXTEEN MILLION MUTANTS.

IT WOULD HAVE KILLED *ALL* OF US.

MAY POSTERITY *FORGIVE* ME.

MAY OUR DRY CLEANERS FORGIVE YOU, CHARLES, DEAR.

MAY GOD AWARD YOU A *MEDAL* FOR YOUR UNINHIBITED MARKMANSHIP.

HARDCORE, CHUCK.

I HAD TO PUT A STOP TO IT, LOGAN. I WON'T ALLOW ANY MORE MUTANTS TO *DIE.*

THINGS MUST *CHANGE* NOW.

TO ME, MY X-MEN.

A HORRIFIED WORLD REACTS TO THE MUTANT GENOCIDE IN GENOSHA--

NOW CHANGING STEREOTYPED PORTRAYALS OF MUTANTS IN MOVIES AND ON T.V.--

Live   *NEWS*

"MOST MUTANTS ARE DECENT LAW-ABIDING PEOPLE," ADMIT LAW ENFORCEMENT AGENCIES.

RENOWNED MUTANT EXPERT PROFESSOR CHARLES XAVIER NOW BELIEVES MAN AND HIS GENETIC COUSINS MUST REACH A NEW UNDERSTANDING IN THE WAKE OF THIS TERRIBLE TRAGEDY.

WHY IS HE DOING THESE TALK SHOWS?

PEOPLE ARE TALKING.

I DON'T KNOW. DOES HE SEEM MILDLY TRAUMATIZED TO YOU?

DOESN'T *EVERYTHING* SEEM MILDLY TRAUMATIZED TO YOU, SCOTT?

THERE'S BLOOD ON THE WALLS, HANK'S IN SHOCK...

AND SCOTT.
PLEASE.

I CAN'T STAND YOU BEING SO *DISTANT* ALL THE TIME. IT'S DRIVING ME MAD...

I... I CAN'T MAKE IT FEEL LIKE IT *USED* TO...IT'S NOT...

WHAT'S THE POINT OF IT ALL COMING OUT *WRONG?*

READ MY *MIND,* JEAN.

NO.

READ MY LIPS, *NOTHING* WILL EVER BREAK THE BOND BETWEEN US. WE *BOTH* KNOW THAT.

BUT WE'VE BARELY TOUCHED ONE ANOTHER FOR FIVE MONTHS.

AND RIGHT NOW THIS MARRIAGE FEELS VERY STRANGE AND COLD, SCOTT.

POST CARD

JEAN...

...WHEN EN SABAH NUR WAS IN MY HEAD, HE SPENT A LOT OF HIS TIME STRIPPING AWAY A FEW OF MY ILLUSIONS ABOUT LIFE AND ABOUT *MYSELF.*

I REALIZED HOW MANY OF MY HIGH IDEALS ARE JUST BASED ON SELF-INTEREST AND SELF-DECEPTION.

I DENIED IT, OF COURSE. I *BEAT* HIM IN THE END, LIKE WE ALWAYS DO, AND I CAST HIM OUT OF MY THOUGHTS...

...BUT THE THING IS, I JUST CAN'T SEEM TO CAST *HIS* THOUGHTS OUT OF *ME.*

YOU'RE NOT THE ONLY PERSON WHO WAS EVER POSSESSED BY AN EVIL SPIRIT, SCOTT...

...THE BAD FEELING GOES *AWAY.*

I DON'T KNOW IF I *FEEL* BAD, JEAN.

I JUST FEEL AND DIFFERENT, THAT'S ALL, AND I DON'T WANT TO HURT YOU OR ANYONE. BUT...

--WITH THAT IN MIND, I FEEL THAT IT'S FINALLY TIME TO PUT AN END TO *MASKS.* AN END TO HIDING OUR GIFTS BEHIND "SECRET IDENTITIES" AND ILL-FITTING CLOTHES.

OH MY GOD... SCOTT...

...WHAT'S HE *DOING?*

HE *CAN'T* DO THIS...

LADIES AND GENTLEMEN.

MY NAME IS CHARLES XAVIER, ALSO KNOWN AS PROFESSOR X.

AND I AM A MUTANT.

NEW X-MEN #117
COVER ARTWORK

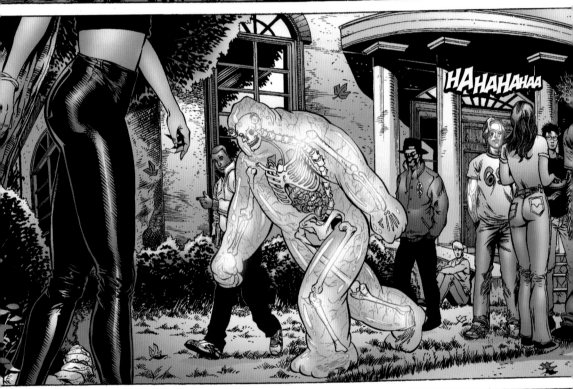

WE BOTH KNOW THE DEAL. *WE* ALWAYS HAVE.

IT WOULD NEVER WORK BETWEEN US.

MY STUDENTS INSISTED I *WITNESS* THIS SPECTACLE.

WHERE EXACTLY SHOULD I BE AIMING THESE PRYING LENSES, *SCOTT,* DEAR?

TRY YOUR *LEFT.* A LITTLE MORE TOWARDS THE HUGE ALIEN SPACESHIP HOVERING OVER THE TREES, *EMMA.*

THIS ENTIRE OPERATION HAS BEEN *SECRET* FOR YEARS.

AND YOU CHOSE NOW FOR THE X-MEN TO GO *PUBLIC*? IS THIS REALLY *WISE*?

HUMAN PROTESTS WILL FADE WHEN THEY SEE WE HAVE NOTHING TO HIDE AND MUCH TO *OFFER* THEM.

MUTANTS HAVE LIVED IN *FEAR* AND COWERED BEHIND MASKS FOR TOO LONG.

WE HAVE FIVE PERMANENT TEACHING STAFF ALONG WITH FIELD AGENTS.

THERE ARE CURRENTLY ONE HUNDRED AND FIFTY-TWO PUPILS, ALL MUTANTS.

BEHIND THE WOOD-PANELLED WALLS, BENEATH THE POLISHED FLOOR-BOARDS OF THE *XAVIER INSTITUTE* LIES A STATE-OF-THE-ART MUTANT LOCATION AND RESCUE FACILITY.

I SENSE THE TIDE OF HISTORY TURNING...

WHAT WAS YOU WANTED TO *SEE* ME ABOUT HENRY...?

...SHOULDN'T YOU BE ON YOUR *DATE*?

OH, I DECIDED THAT THE CHARMS OF A VIRTUAL *AUTOPSY* FAR OUTWEIGHED THOSE OF A ROMANTIC BALLOON RIDE WITH MYSELF.

HER *REAL* BODY'S STILL IN DEEP FREEZE, BUT I MADE THIS COMPUTER DISSECTION MODEL OF THE *CASSANDRA NOVA ENTITY* SHORTLY AFTER SHE ALMOST KILLED US ALL.

AND...? WHAT IS IT, HENRY?

YOU CROSS-REFERENCED CASSANDRA NOVA'S *DNA* WIT CEREBRA'S GENETIC LIBRAR FILES, DIDN'T YOU...?

YES, THAT'S EXACTLY RIGHT. I WANTED TO SEE IF WE HAD ENCOUNTERED ANYTHING LIKE HER *BEFORE*, AND...

GGHHAAU!!!

AUURRR!

YOU'RE A WORTHLESS, *FAILED* EXPERIMENT AND YOU BROUGHT IT ALL ON YOURSELF.

IS THIS YOUR SPECIAL MUTANT *"GIFT"* MANIFESTING ITSELF, HENRY?

THIS SLOW CRAWL BACKWARDS *DOWN* THE EVOLUTIONARY SPIRAL?

WHERE WILL YOUR *"GIFT"* TAKE YOU *NEXT,* I WONDER?

WILL YOU BECOME AN INSECT? A *WORM?*

A SLITHERING, INCOHERENT SLIME MOLD STILL TRYING TO CHARM HUMAN WOMEN WITH ITS AWKWARD POETRY?

I... I AM A MEMBER OF THE EVOLVED SPECIES *HOMO SAPIENS SUPERIOR*...

I... I... HAVE A DOCTORATE DEGREE! I CAN TURN THE PERIODIC TABLE INTO A DIRTY RHYME IF THAT'S WHAT IT TAKES TO GET YOU OUT...

♪

I HAVE TO SAY, I'VE SEEN *BETTER* ON THE CINEMA SCREEN.

EVENING, EMMA, SCOTT. WHY ARE THERE SO MANY STUDENT OUT OF THEIR BED AND RUNNING AROU THE HALLS WITH CAMERAS?

THEY ALL WANT PICTURES OF THE SHI'AR FLAGSHIP.

IT'S NOT EVERY DAY MOST PEOPLE GET TO SEE SOMETHING LIKE THAT.

SOME OF THE HUMAN MEDIA HAVE BEEN CALLING IT A *"PROVOCATIVE"* DISPLAY.

LET THEM SAY WHAT THEY LIKE, EMMA..

I'M *PROUD* OF THE FACT THAT MUTANTS WERE AMONG THE FIRST TO MAKE CONTACT WITH EXTRA-TERRESTRIAL CULTURES.

OUR RECORD FOR TOLERATING THE UNKNOWN HAS ALWAYS BEEN EXEMPLARY.

To be continued in NEW X-MEN: IMPERIAL
(Volume 24 of the Ultimate Marvel Graphic Novel Collection)

THE WRITER

Grant Morrison

COMICBOOK SHAMAN

Born in Glasgow on January 31, 1960, **Grant Morrison** is one of the few British writers who did not get his big US break after first working for **2000 AD**. Whilst he did go on to write for the British S weekly, his road to comicbook superstardom was a tad convoluted beginning in 1978 with contributions to a UK alternative comic *Near Myths*, for which he drew two of his four stories.

Near Myths foundered after just five issues but Morrison was already building his CV. As well as producing a weekly strip about an unemployed Glaswegian superhero for local newspapers, he was also writing for *Starblazer*, a science fiction companion to Dundee-based **DC Thomson's** digest-sized *Commando*.

But comics weren't an all-consuming passion for Morrison, at least not during his early days. He also played rhythm guitar with *The Mixers*, a band with which he toured during the early 1980s. Subsequently he wrote for *Warrior* as well as several **Marvel UK** titles while continuing with contributions to *Starblazer*.

In 1986 his work began appearing in *2000 AD*, where *Zenith*, his first shot at deconstructing the superhero genre premiered the following year. That series brought him to the attention of **DC**, where he made his US debut on *Animal Man*, a series into which he inserted himself. It was there that his talent for nonlinear narratives and his counter-cultural leanings began to reveal themselves.

A playwright and an occultist as well as a comicbook writer, Morrison continued to work for DC until 2001. During that time, he took over *Doom Patrol* – transforming that mundane superteam title into a surrealistic tour-de-force – and wrote *Arkham Asylum: A Serious House on Serious Earth*, an innovative 1989 graphic novel in which Morrison experimented with symbolic writing.

Aside from his DC work, he continued to be involved in the UK comics scene. In 1993 Morrison, fellow Glaswegian comic writer **Mark Millar** and **John Smith** were asked to reinvigorate 2000 AD for an eight-week run called *The Summer Offensive*. The same year DC launched **Vertigo**, its mature readers imprint which published several of Morrison's creator owned properties, amongst them *Flex Mentallo*. This Charles Atlas-inspired 1996 *Doom Patrol* spin-off was drawn by **Frank Quitely**, an artist who would feature strongly in Morrison's career in the future. At Vertigo Morrison also launched *The Invisibles*, which many consider to be his magnum opus. Premiering in 1994, the idiosyncratic series was heavily influenced by the writings of **Robert Anton Wilson**, **Aleister Crowley** and **William Burroughs** and Morrison's practice of chaos magic. It ran 59 issues across three volumes until 2000.

Two years prior to the debut of *The Invisibles*, the

writer had made a return to the world of DC's superheroes with *Aztek, the Ultimate Man* – a short-lived series he co-wrote with Millar with whom he also collaborated on a short run on *The Flash* – and *DC One Million*, a 1998 four-parter that was at the core of a major DCU event. However Morrison really made an impact on the DC Universe when he was asked to revamp the *Justice League of America*. Relaunching the Big Seven heroes in 1997's *JLA #1*, Morrison brought the team – which consisted of Superman, Batman, Wonder Woman et al – back to its best-selling status across the 41 issues of his run. That ended in 2000, the year in which he worked again with Quitely, on the hardcover *JLA: Earth Two* graphic novel.

With the new millennium just beginning and his DC work coming to a end, Morrison moved to Marvel where – together with Quitely – he took over *X-Men*; the title being renamed *New X-Men* to acknowledge his plans for a radical overhaul of the House of Ideas' mutant team, which – he said – would become a social sci-fi book, not a superhero comic. His revamp was a major critical and commercial success. It was also a defining moment in his career; it established him as one of only a handful of creators whose name attached to a title could guarantee sales.

Morrison stayed on *New X-Men* until 2004. It wasn't his first Marvel work; previously he'd written *Skrull Kill Crew* (a 1995 collaboration with Millar). It also wasn't his only 21st century project for the House of Ideas. Before he left to return to DC, he added *Marvel Boy* (2000) and *Fantastic Four 1234* (2001) to his credits.

In the last ten years, Morrison has produced a flurry of different titles for DC/Vertigo ranging from *The Filth* (2002) and *WE3* (2004) to *Batman* (2006) and *All-Star Superman* (2008). Recently, Morrison has become the driving force behind DC's super hero comics. He is intimately involved with the drastic reshaping which has effectively reset the entire universe back to its very beginnings, allowing new origins to be told for a vast majority of the company's characters.

With his vast back catalogue highly experimental and unorthodox attitude towards writing comics, Grant Morrison is one of an elite band whose work is always guaranteed to be a huge commercial and critical success. His every move and utterance is minutely examined and he has the power and vision to help shape the comics medium as it moves further into the 21st century.

MAGIC MAN

Morrison's interest in the occult and position as a self confessed Chaos Magician has made him something of a counter-culture icon. His books often contain themes and ideas inspired by his studies of various spiritual and magical teaching from around the world. One of the strangest uses for his occult knowledge was in 2005 when he was asked by popstar **Robbie Williams** to design the artwork for his latest album *Intensive Care*. Along with artist **Frank Quitely,** Morrison created an album cover littered with various magical sigils and symbols, including a set of tarot card designs all featuring Robbie Williams.

Interestingly, this was not to be Morrison's only association with the world of rock and roll. He has also recently worked closely with **Gerard Way** of **My Chemical Romance** fame, even appearing in the video for the band's 2011 single *Art Is The Weapon*.

THE ARTIST

Frank Quitely

IT DIDN'T take Vincent Deighan that long to hit the big time. Prior to getting together with **Grant Morrison** to illustrate the Glasgow-born writer's 1996 Vertigo four-parter *Flex Mentallo*, the comics experience of the artist better known these days as Frank Quitely had been limited. Deighan had started out in the early '90s writing and drawing *The Greens* for *Electric Soup*, a Scottish underground anthology. Concerned that his family might take offence at his strip – a beautifully rendered parody of *The Broons*, a long-running and much-respected weekly *DC Thomson* newspaper humour strip centring on an archetypal tenement-dwelling Scottish family – he adopted a pseudonym and has worked as Frank Quitely ever since. As he quite frankly explained, "I changed my name so my mum and dad couldn't see me writing this stuff at the time because I was scared of their reaction."

Although he is now a comicbook superstar, it wasn't the Glasgow-born artist's intention to make a career out of drawing comics. "I got into comics by accident after I was kicked out of art school. I wish I had some amazing story but I just squandered the opportunity. I probably went too young. I had the idea that you would do art school and get taught to draw and paint - because that's what I wanted to do. Ideally just to be a painter – doing drawings and paintings and prints, and getting in galleries."

Despite his having other plans, *The Greens* brought Quitely to the attention of the *Judge Dredd Megazine* and he drew several strips for the *2000 AD* companion title during 1993 and 1994, which was when America first beckoned. As well as contributing to *The Big Book*

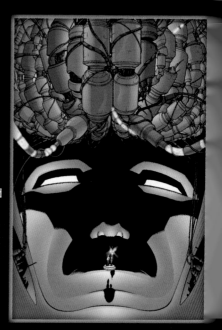

of Weirdos, *The Big Book of Death* and several other such **Paradox Press** titles, Quitely also drew a Robbie – no relation to Grant – Morrison-written three-parter for *Dark Horse Presents*.

Then Grant Morrison asked him to draw *Flex Mentallo*, which was tagged Man of Muscle Mystery. "I was blown away by the script, and pulled out all the stops in order to pass on as much as possible to the reader, and although it bears many of the hallmarks of an inexperienced young artist trying desperately to punch above his weight,

there's a naive, earnest, honesty about the artwork that suits what the story is actually getting at.

"I remember," added the unique and talented artist, "in one of those early meetings we had, I told Grant that I didn't know anything about the superheroes and eras that were being referenced, and he said that was why he had picked me, because he didn't want somebody who would 'get it'."

While *Flex Mentallo* may have been the first Morrison/Quitely collaboration, it was far from the last. Over the next 15 years or so writer and artist worked together on ever-more commercially successful and critically acclaimed projects.

On the one hand there has been *We3* – an innovative 2004 **Vertigo** three-parter – while 2000's *JLA: Earth 2* graphic novel and the back-to-basics *All Star Superman* (which ran from 2006 to

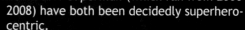

2008) have both been decidedly superhero-centric.

Although Quitely's name is closely linked with that of his Glaswegian writing partner, the artist has not solely worked with Morrison over the past decade and a half. He has also collaborated with fellow Scot **Alan Grant** on *Batman: The Scottish Connection* (a 1998 one-shot), with **Jamie Delano** on Vertigo's *2020 Visions* in 1997 and with another Glaswegian writer, **Mark Millar** on *The Authority* between 2000 and 2001. He left that ultra-violent and controversial **DC/WildStorm** series to work again with Morrison on a *New X-Men* run at **Marvel.** That ended in 2003.

Much in demand these days as a cover artist, Quitely is currently working on a yet-to-be-announced collaboration with Morrison – whom he also partnered on *Batman and Robin* in 2009 – and another with Millar. His detailed, economical style will ensure he remains a fan-favourite artist for years to come.

ART GALLERY

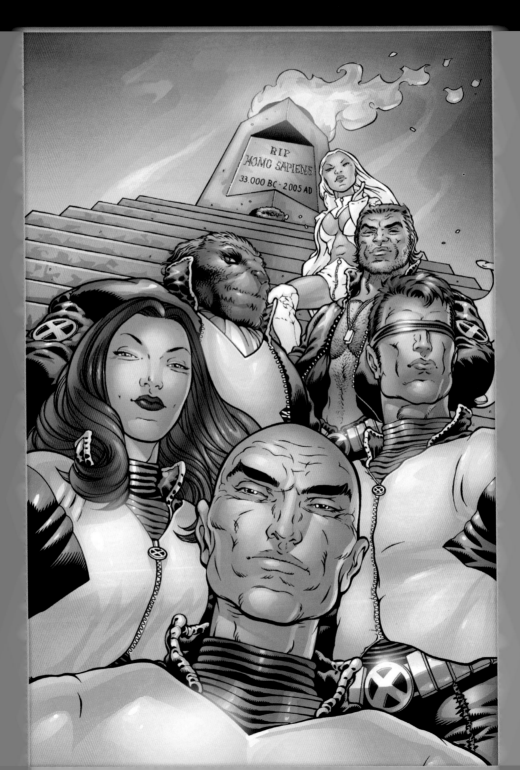

Cyclops

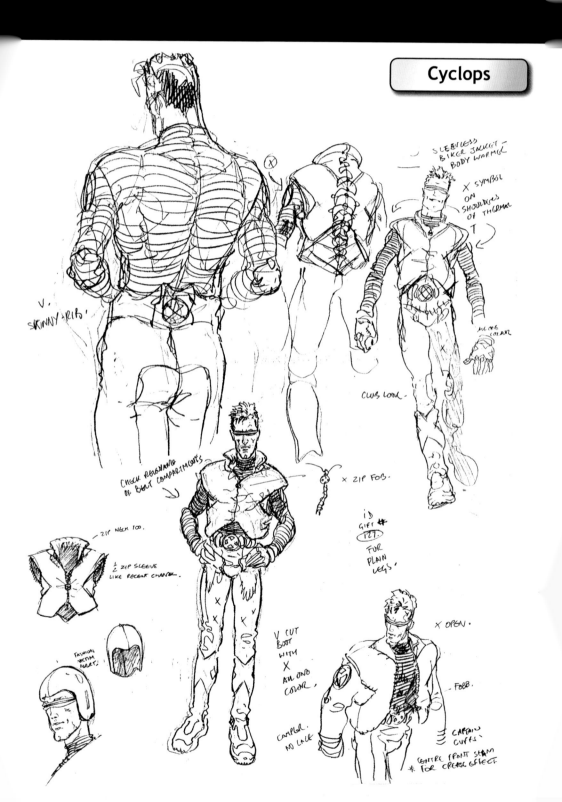

Team Line-up

Wolverine

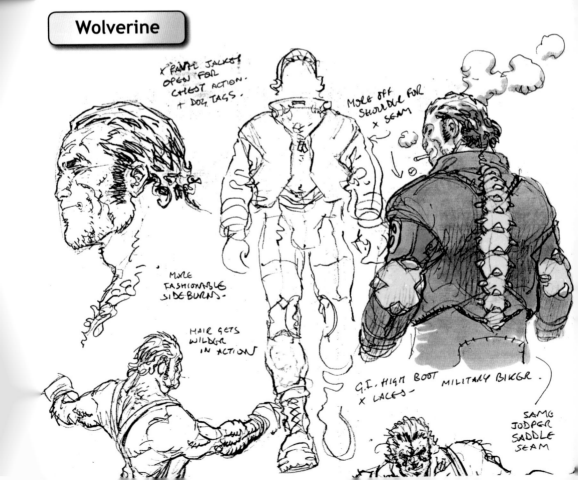

X PANAL JACKS? OPEN FOR CHEST ACTION. + DOZ TAGS.

MORE OFF SHOULDER FOR X SEAM

MORE FASHIONABLE SIDEBURNS.

HAIR GETS WILDER IN ACTION

G.I. HIGH BOOT X LACES.

MILITARY BIKER.

SAME JODPER SADDLE SEAM

NAKED X FRONT

X ONE PIECE

FRONT   BACK
REVERSE

@ BACK OF THIS ↓

E.W.S.
SORFEND MASK

DIFFERENT OUTFIT FOR EVERY SCENE
RIDING, OFFICE, SCHOOL, EVENING, SEX

SPEC LEN OF

SPECS WITH COLOURED
LENSES FOR ONLY SPARK
OF COLOUR. X 24 FOR.

STILHETTOS
PUMPS
RED RIDING HOOD

SCENE

THE WRITER

How Grant Morrison reinvented the X-Men for the 21st Century

E IS FOR EVOLUTION

In July 2001 **Grant Morrison** took over the reins of *X-Men* and managed to revolutionise the titular mutants in spectacular fashion. How did he manage this feat? Rather fittingly, he let the X-Men evolve.

Rewind to before he picked up his pen and, like any writer worth their salt, Morrison first immersed himself in X-Men lore. Taking it to the extreme, as with everything he does, he feverishly read through every single X-Men graphic novel available. A fan since his teenage years, this only served to confirm his suspicions that his own favourite run, that of **Chris Claremont** and **John Byrne** in the late 70s, were the X-tales that worked best.

As the era responsible for such classic stories as the *Dark Phoenix* and *Days of Future Past* sagas, Morrison saw that Claremont and Byrne "had the freedom to create new material, reconceptualise the old stuff which still worked and ignore the outmoded elements which had sapped the original of its vitality." Using this as his mantra he set about stripping the franchise back to what he saw as its core concept: New/good Vs. Old/bad.

COSTUME CHANGE

With his first bold step the name of the comic was changed from plain *X-Men* to *New X-Men*. This was to become his calling card for the entire run. This would be a series with new heroes, new villains, new takes on old characters and ideas. Even new uniforms.

Out were the super-hero style blue and gold outfits, in was cool black leather with 'X' emblazoned in day-glo yellow. This was another sign of what Morrison was planning: a series that was as much soap as spectacle, a chance to really get under the skin of a bunch of fabulous looking people who just happened to have amazing powers.

And what about those people? Over the 40 years of their existence the ranks of the X-Men had grown quite considerably, and it was starting to get tricky keeping track of who was who. Morrison stripped the team back to an essential five, adding new and old characters into the mix when and where needed, but keeping the focus on the small band. Most importantly,

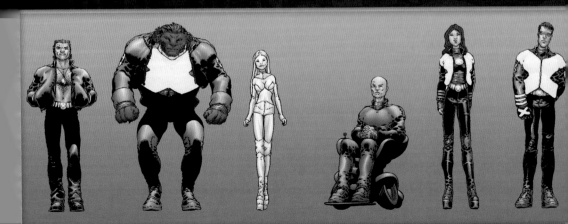

rather than choosing the five with the most pizzazz to their power, the strongest or the strangest, Morrison picked a team comprising of pretty much, in their own different ways, the smartest.

Professor X has rarely seemed more dangerous or more desperate, the reality of being the most dangerous mind on the planet starting to ring true; Beast, fresh from his secondary mutation into a more feline form, plumbed the depths of what it means not just to be different but to feel different; Wolverine, world weary and wise, felt like he was finally beginning to understood the benefits of team-work; Cyclops and Jean Grey had a healthy dollop of realism added to their relationship.

Not content with five of the X-Men's most recognisable faces, Grant Morrison went one step further and added Emma Frost, a former villain, to the ranks who, in the hands of Morrison and *Joss Wheedon* after him, would go on to become one of the decade's most important and popular characters.

SCHOOL DAYS

In the very first issue, Professor X reminds us that "New school term starts Monday." In keeping with all the other changes, Morrison let the school evolve too. When the new term does start, there are throngs of teenage mutants milling about the

X-EPICS

One barrier to gaining the new audience Morrison hoped for was the tendency for past *X-Men* writers to run slow-burning storylines that would sometimes take years to be resolved. To break away from this, he declared that from now on, "Each story arc should be like a movie or TV miniseries... Beginning, middle and end, character development and resolution." He kept his arcs short and punchy but still managed to weave them into a longer whole that offered both accessibility and extended character development.

campus, mutants of all shapes and sizes who are there not to train and become additions to the X-Men roster, but to learn as in any other school (albeit one with blue furry teachers).

Some of the students have 'cool' powers like those of their teachers, others look strange but have no more power than a regular teenager. Adding a dose of real teen angst and youthful rebellion to the melting-pot of ideas that was already brimming over only helped cement *New X-Men* as a must-have title.

By stripping so much away and letting fresh ideas evolve Grant Morrison provided the perfect jumping-in point for the X-Men. He tore up the rulebook of what the team had become and made them exciting and relevant to a whole new generation

FURTHER READING

If you've enjoyed the style and art in this graphic novel, you may be interested in exploring some of these books too.

New X-Men: Imperial
Volume 24 of the
Ultimate Marvel Graphic
Novels Collection
At the book shop:
ISBN: 9780785108870

Skrull Kill Krew

At the book shop:
ISBN: 9780785121206

Marvel Boy

At the book shop:
ISBN: 9780785134404

Fantastic Four: 1234

Wolverine and the X-Men

Marvel Masterworks: X-Men 1977-1978

At the book shop:
ISBN: 9780785158967

At the book shop:
ISBN: 9781846535130

At the book shop:
ISBN: 9781846530098